# PADDINGTON™

## Annual 2015

1 3 5 7 9 10 8 6 4 2

ISBN: 978-0-00-759273-9

First published by HarperCollins Children's Books in 2014

HarperCollins Children's Books is a division of HarperCollins Publishers Ltd.

Text by Mandy Archer

Based on the Paddington novels written and created by Michael Bond

PADDINGTON™ and PADDINGTON BEAR™ © Paddington and Company Limited/STUDIOCANAL S.A. 2014

All non-film images used under licence from Shutterstock

All rights reserved

www.harpercollins.co.uk

Printed and bound in Europe

HarperCollins *Children's Books*

# Contents

# Meet Paddington

Say hello to Paddington! This friendly bear is three feet, six inches tall, with a red hat and a blue duffel coat. He always keeps a marmalade sandwich tucked under his hat — for emergencies!

Paddington was brought up by his devoted Aunt Lucy and Uncle Pastuzo in Darkest Peru. Aunt Lucy told Paddington that if he ever came to Britain, the people there would make him very welcome.

When a terrible earthquake destroyed his rainforest home, Aunt Lucy sent Paddington to London. He stowed away in a lifeboat on a ship bound for the London docks. By the time he arrives at Paddington station, the young bear is tired, lonely and scared. London isn't how he imagined it at all – everyone is in a hurry, they don't say hello or even wear hats!

Paddington is on the brink of a nail-biting adventure when he meets the Brown family — Henry, Mary, Judy and Jonathan.

*" Excuse me? Does anyone know where I can find a home? "*

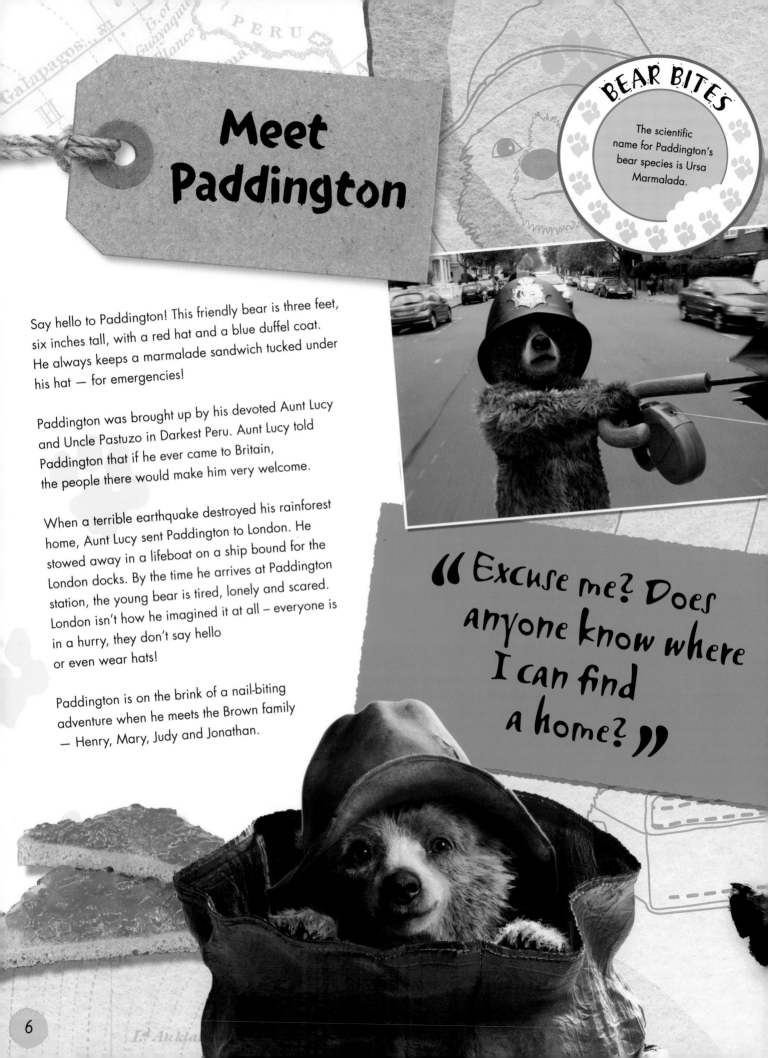

## BEAR BITES

Paddington is particularly fond of his duffel coat. It has a hood for when it rains, wooden toggles for ease of paw and two handy sandwich compartments (or pockets, as we call them!)

## BEAR BITES

Back in Peru, Paddington's family used to make marmalade every year. Aunt Lucy was the best cook in the whole jungle!

# Lost and Found

Paddington station is a scary place for a traveller from Darkest Peru. Paddington doesn't know where to turn! Who might be able to help a young bear in need of a home?

Can you pick out the four objects that don't belong in this picture? Circle each one, then write it down in the spaces below. Now take the first letter of each word and put them together – can you spell out a name?

1. __ __ __ __ __ __ __ __ __

2. __ __ __ __ __

3. __ __ __ __

4. __ __ . __ __

Paddington's first friend in London is called

__ __ __ __.

Paddington can't wait to see London – he wants to visit Buckingham Palace, travel on the underground and finally meet Big Ben! But first, the Brown family are going to take him back to 32 Windsor Gardens.

Oh dear. The taxi driver has got in a muddle with his directions. Choose the right route to the Browns' house.

**Taxi!**

A.

B.

C.

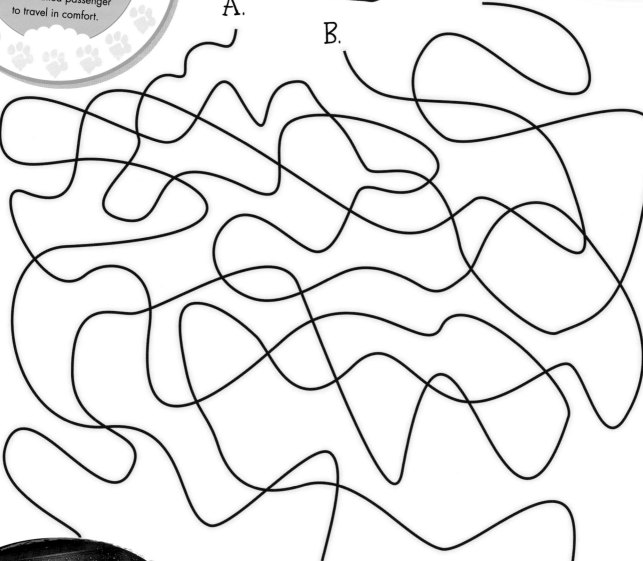

NATURAL HISTORY MUSEUM

WINDSOR GARDENS

← Trafalgar Square

9

# Getting to Know You

Paddington has a lot to get used to — life with the Browns is very different to his home in Darkest Peru. Jonathan and Judy have decided to play some games to get to know their guest and make him feel comfortable. Why don't you join in?

## Whose Shoe?

Split your guests into two teams, then ask everyone to take off one shoe. Each team should then make a pile out of their shoes. Ask each person from one team to pick a random shoe from the other team's pile and then find the person that the shoe belongs to. When they've matched up the footwear with its rightful owner, the pair should ask each other a question about themselves. Keep going until the first team's pile is finished. Afterwards the other team should do the same with their pile of shoes.

## Human Bingo

This is a great game for a larger gathering. Draw a grid with at least one 20 squares. Write a question into each square that at least one of your guests would be able to answer 'yes' to. Questions such as 'have you been to Paris?', 'can you play the flute?' or 'do you have a guinea pig?' might all work. Photocopy or print off the grid if you did it on a computer and give everyone a copy and a pencil. Your friends must walk around the room, finding a person who says 'yes' to each box. They must then ask them to tick and sign the box before moving on. The winner is the first person to score a 'full house' of signatures!

## Perfect Pairs

This game works best for larger groups. Think of some famous pairs. How about Mickey and Minnie or Batman and Robin? Write each name down on a sticky note, then stick one on each of your guest's foreheads. The guests must travel around the room, trying to guess their identity by asking questions about themselves. They can ask anything at all, as long as the question can only have a 'yes' or 'no' answer. After everyone has worked out who they are, they must then seek out their partner.

## Secret Sticker

Give each of your guests a sheet of stickers. Each person in the room has to get rid of their entire sheet by secretly sticking them onto the other guests, one sticker at a time, without being caught. The first person to wave a clean sheet is the winner.

## Tall Truths

Give everyone a sheet of paper and a pen. Ask your guests to write three things about themselves. It is important that two are true and one is made-up. Now sit in a circle and take turns to read out your statements without laughing. After each person has spoken, vote on what was fact and what was fiction. You might be surprised by the results!

## BEAR BITES

If all else fails when you meet someone new, talk about the weather – it's Britain's favourite pastime! There are weather records for this nation dated all the way back to 55BC.

Paddington is a loyal nephew – he always remembers to write to his Aunt Lucy back at the Home for Retired Bears in Peru. Look at his latest batch of postcards. Can you work out what places Paddington has been visiting in London?

Read each postcard, then match it to the correct London landmark.

# Postcards to Peru

**3.**

To my adoring Aunt,

I met my delightful new friend Mr Gruber this morning. We visited an old building with an impressive domed roof. It was designed by an architect called Sir Christopher Wren.

Paddington x

Aunt Lucy,

Home for Retired Bears

Lima

Peru

Dear Aunt Lucy,

Today Judy and Jonathan took me on an enormous Ferris wheel. Instead of carriages, we rode in giant glass pods. What breathtaking views!

Paddington X

Aunt Lucy,

Home for Retired Bears

Lima

Peru

**4.**

Dear Aunt Lucy,

This evening Mrs Brown decided that it was time for some culture! We watched a Shakespeare play in an open-air venue on the banks of the River Thames. Bravo!

Paddington x

Aunt Lucy,

Home for Retired Bears

Lima

Peru

**2.**

Hello from London!

The city does have such a lot of history! Today I went to its very centre. I paddled in fountains and saluted Admiral Nelson. He was standing at the top of his very own column!

Paddington x

Aunt Lucy,

Home for Retired Bears

Lima

Peru

A.  The Globe Theatre          postcard ☐

B.  St Paul's Cathedral        postcard ☐

C.  The London Eye            postcard ☐

D.  Trafalgar Square          postcard ☐

# Meet Henry Brown

Henry Brown takes his role as father very seriously. Every day he works in an office, working out the odds of bad stuff happening. When he gets home, he focuses all his energy on keeping the Browns safe. That means no jumping, shouting or doing anything impulsive. Ever. It can seem boring and annoying, but Henry only does it because he loves them all so much and he wants to protect them.

When Paddington arrives, everything changes. Before Henry has even had the chance of adding him to the house insurance policy, the young bear has caused havoc. And despite himself, Henry also starts taking risks, breaking into filing systems and impersonating a cleaning lady!

## BEAR BITES

By day Henry works as a risk analyst. Having a bear in the house increases the chances of fire, flood and pestilence by 4000%.

## BEAR BITES

Mr Brown likes his life to be orderly. His stationery drawer is so carefully arranged, he has even drawn white lines on the bottom of it to show where each object should go.

*"The bear is not sleeping in anyone's room. He's going in the attic and I want you all to lock your doors."*

## BEAR BITES

It is Mary Brown that gives Paddington his English name. Paddington's real Peruvian name is a funny kind of growl that humans would find very difficult to pronounce.

# Meet Mary Brown

> **" Well then, Paddington, how would you like to come home with us? "**

Henry's wife Mary is the very opposite of her husband – a creative, open-minded woman who's always ready to think the best of people. As soon as she reads the plea on Paddington's luggage label, 'Please look after this bear. Thank you', she is determined to look after him. She insists on giving the small bear tea and then bringing him back to 32 Windsor Gardens.

Paddington takes to Mary at once, but not everybody in the family is a fan of her free-spirited ways. She has a fondness for nicknames that make her daughter Judy cringe.

Back in Peru, a family is a tribe that works together as a group, but the Browns aren't like that at all when Paddington first arrives. If Mary's hunch is right however, Paddington might just help to change all that…

## BEAR BITES

Mary illustrates adventure stories. Her latest book is set in the old tunnels and sewers that run underneath London.

15

# Paddington's Grand Tour of London

## The London Docks

This is where my adventure in Britain began. I travelled from Lima to the docks in a giant ship, taking care to hide out of sight. It was a long journey, but Aunt Lucy packed lots of jars of marmalade to keep me going.

## Paddington Station

I arrived here in a mail sack, looking for a home. Luckily, the Browns found me! Paddington is a fine old station. It was designed by a very famous engineer called Isambard Kingdom Brunel. The first underground station was opened here in 1863.

## The Serpentine

The Serpentine is a lake in the middle of Hyde Park. Mrs Brown comes to swim here. She says that the Serpentine Swimming Club is the oldest swimming club in Britain. They hold a famous race every Christmas day. Even though the water is terribly cold, the racers aren't allowed to wear wetsuits.

## Portobello Road

The Browns introduced me to Mr Gruber. His wonderful emporium, Gruber's Antiques, is on the Portobello Road. It's a street full of hustle and bustle, especially on Saturdays when market traders set up their stalls.

### Buckingham Palace

The home of Her Majesty, Queen Elizabeth II, and a very fine place indeed. The sentries on guard here are particularly well-bred – one even shared his sandwich with me!

### Big Ben

When I was a happy-go-lucky treehouse bear I dreamed of meeting Big Ben! Imagine my surprise when I discovered that Big Ben isn't a real person. It's actually the nickname of the bell inside the clock tower. The building itself is called the Elizabeth Tower – I'm told that even many Londoners don't know that!

### The Natural History Museum

What a wonderful institution! This magnificent building is packed to the rafters with fossils, plants and dinosaur bones.

### The London Underground

This is how most Londoners get around the city – on trains underground. Riding the Tube is rather difficult for a bear, though – the barriers are a little quick for me!

# Please look after this Bear. THANK YOU

Paddington thinks luggage labels are so useful, he's made some more! Unfortunately, the young bear has got a little confused with his letters. Can you work out who each label is for? Unscramble the anagrams — there are clues to help you if you get stuck.

**1.**

## LMLITECNI

_ _ _ _ _ _ _ _ _

Quick clue: Director of the Natural History Museum.

**2.**

## RM RYCRU

_ _   _ _ _ _ _

Quick clue: The Browns' nosy neighbour.

**3.**

## EYHRN OBWNR

_ _ _ _ _   _ _ _ _ _

Quick clue: A well-spoken English gentleman.

**5.**

## JAHNNTOA

_ _ _ _ _ _ _ _

Quick clue: A 10-year-old who dreams of travelling into space.

**4.**

## RSM RDIB

_ _ _   _ _ _ _

Quick clue: An elderly lady with naval connections.

### Bonus bear brainteaser

What is the name of Paddington's uncle?

_ _ _ _ _ _ _

18

Usually Paddington doesn't have very much in his suitcase, apart from a few jars of marmalade! Today Mrs Bird has popped a few extra bits and pieces inside. Set your stopwatch to 60 seconds, then study the objects very carefully. When the time's up, flip the page and take Paddington's observation quiz. Only the sharpest puzzlers will be able to bag full marks!

# Suitcase Surprise

1. How many objects are on the front of the apron?
   What are they?

   ......................................................................

2. How many jars of marmalade did you count?

   ......................................................................

3. What item might hold a boat steady?

   ......................................................................

4. Is the lining of the suitcase patterned or plain?

   ......................................................................

5. What colour is the book's front cover?

   ......................................................................

6. What might stop water from draining away?

   ......................................................................

7. How many flags did you see?

   ......................................................................

8. Which object comes from the garden?

   ......................................................................

9. How many cameras did you see?

   ......................................................................

WANTED ON VOYAGE

Director of Taxidermy at the Natural History Museum, Millicent, has used her cunning intellect to set you a word challenge. Each of the terms below are made up of two existing words joined together. Take 'smoke' and 'fog' as an example – together they combine to form 'smog'.

# Millicent's Mix-Ups

Can you find the original pair at the heart of each of the hybrid words below? All the words you need are waiting at the bottom of the page.

1. ZEEDONK

..................................... and .....................................

2. HELIPORT

..................................... and .....................................

3. SITCOM

..................................... and .....................................

4. JEGGINGS

..................................... and .....................................

5. PIXEL

..................................... and .....................................

6. BRUNCH

..................................... and .....................................

7. MOPED

..................................... and .....................................

8. CAMCORDER

..................................... and .....................................

9. ESCALATOR

..................................... and .....................................

10. LABRADOODLE

..................................... and .....................................

BREAKFAST    LEGGINGS    PICTURE    ELEVATOR

MOTOR    ELEMENT    LABRADOR

JEANS    LUNCH    SITUATION

POODLE    AIRPORT    ESCALATE    COMEDY

ZEBRA    DONKEY    CAMERA

HELICOPTER    PEDAL    RECORDER

## BEAR BITES
When two words are combined to create a new meaning, the new term is called a portmanteau.

Can you think up your own funny portmanteau? Write it here.

..................................

# Paddington's Scrapbook

Paddington has gathered some of his favourite photographs together and put them in an album. Whenever he feels sad or lonely, Paddington can go up to the Browns' attic and cheer himself up again!

Paddington needs to write some captions for these pages, but Mrs Bird has called him down for tea. Could you finish the job for him? Write an imaginative description underneath each shot. The first one has been done for you.

The Brown family were very ...................... welcoming when I arrived in London. ..................

The calypso band... .......................................
.......................................

Judy... ...........................................

Me... .......................................................

.......................................................................

£3·20M

SHOWN

GLE

9·SEP·10

DOORS OPEN AT.

17:00

THE TICKET IS SOLD UNDER LICENCE OF THE EVENT GROUP AND REMAINS THE PROPERTY AND CAN NOT BE RESOLD.

19·SEP·10

Route
ANY PERMITTED

Validity
ON DATE SHOWN

SINGLE

Printed 17·44 on 19·SEP·10

Mr Curry...

Mr Gruber's shop...

## Super scrapbooking

ADMIT
ONE

251496

Starting a scrapbook is easy – all you need is an album or journal – even a lined exercise book will do! Here are Paddington's tips for recording your own magical memories.

### 1. Stick, stick, stick!

A scrapbook doesn't have to be limited to photos. Postcards, ticket stubs, stickers and leaflets will all make your pages interesting to read and look back on.

### 2. Decorate the pages.

Use ink stamps, felt pens and crayons to fill up any spare space with notes, cartoons and pictures. It's a chance to really get creative!

### 3. Save the date!

Whenever you can remember the date of an event or special occasion, write it in your scrapbook. When you look back in the future, it will help you place how old you were when it happened.

# Tea-time Teaser

Paddington is very partial to afternoon tea — it is one of his favourite things about living with the Browns. If marmalade sandwiches are on the menu, he's even more delighted! Can you help the hungry bear complete this crossword puzzle? Use the clues to help you fill it with tasty treats.

## ACROSS

3. Paddington's all-time favourite food.
6. Long green salad vegetable that is sliced and served in sandwiches.
7. Pastry with Scandinavian origins.
9. Small round cake often served with cream and jam.
10. Savoury sandwich ingredient often served with cress.
11. Describes a bun that is glazed with sugar and makes your fingers feel gluey.

## DOWN

1. Grilled bread that Paddington eats with lashings of butter.
2. Sweetener for hot drinks, added by the teaspoon.
3. White, puffy dessert made from whipped egg whites.
4. Treat with a hole in the middle, often filled with jam.
5. Type of lemon spread that is used in lemon meringue pie.
8. Both bees and bears enjoy eating this.
12. An alternative to tea.

## Tea for two?

In the early 1800s, most people only ate two meals a day – breakfast and dinner in the evening. It is thought that one of Queen Victoria's closest friends, the Duchess of Bedford, first suggested eating a mid afternoon snack to keep hunger pangs away until evening time. She invited others to join her for tea, cakes and sandwiches. By the mid 1850s, afternoon tea was an established tradition all over England.

**BEAR BITES**

In order to make just one jar of honey, hard-working honey bees have to buzz the equivalent of three times around the world.

# Paddington's Paper Caper

When Paddington needs to search for answers at the Geographer's Guild, Mr Brown's the man to help him. Can you help them to break into the building and find the secret files from Peru? Find a friend, then play this game to find out!

**1 START**

**2**

**3** Get lost in the Guild's lobby. Miss a turn.

**4**

**5** Give your opponent a 'Hard Stare'. Fix their gaze without blinking for 10 seconds, then move to square 10.

**6**

**7**

**8**

**9** Name the capital city of Peru. If you get the answer right, throw again.

**10**

**11**

**12** Sweet-talk the receptionist. Move to the next even number.

**13**

**14**

**15** Your path gets blocked. Move back five spaces.

**16**

**17** Smuggle yourself in as a cleaner. Throw again.

**18**

**19**

**20**

# How to play

1. Trace the counters here on to a sheet of white card and cut them out, then colour them in. Or you can use existing counters or coins. Find a die.
2. Choose a counter each, then place them on to the first square of the game board.
3. The youngest player throws first. Take turns moving along the board following the instructions as you go. The winner is the first player to make it all the way to the finish.

**37**

**38**

**39**
Fall down the Guild steps with the film in your pocket. Go all the way back to the START.

**40**
**FINISH**

**35**
Can you name three species of bear? Move one space forward for every one you get right.

**36**

**34**

**33**
Find a suspicious reel of film. Stuff it into your pocket and move forward one space.

**30**
You lose your marmalade sandwich. Miss two turns.

**29**

**31**

**32**

**27**
A guard approaches. Move back to 23.

**28**

**26**

**25**
You are challenged by a Guild member. Name three rivers, then throw again.

**21**
Get paw prints over the secret files. Don't move on until you throw a six.

**22**

**23**

**24**

27

# Ursa Marmalada

Ursa Marmalada is a fascinating bear. Although small in stature, it is remarkably intelligent. It can be taught to walk on two legs, read and even speak English! Paddington is an especially fine example. He has warm brown fur, twinkly eyes and a shiny black nose.

Stay scissor safe! Ask an adult to help before starting this make-it.

Would you like your own furry Paddington bear? This tissue paper make-it would look great on any bedroom shelf or wall.

**YOU WILL NEED:**

- Old newspapers
- Poster paints
- Paint brush
- Small paper bowl
- Pencil
- White cardboard
- PVA glue
- Large paper plate
- White tissue paper
- Stick-on wobbly eyes
- Black and red felt

1. Spread out some old newspapers on a dry work surface, then take out the small paper bowl. The bowl will become Paddington's muzzle. Use your brush to paint the bowl all over in a light, golden brown.

2. The large paper plate will be Paddington's face.
   Paint the back of the plate all over in a darker brown.

3. Draw two circular ear-shapes onto the cardboard and cut them out.
   Paint both of these light brown. When all the pieces are dry,
   glue the ears on to the **front** of the large paper plate.

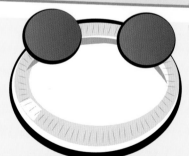

4. Turn the plate over and stick the painted muzzle in the centre at the bottom.
   Paddington is starting to take shape!

5. Now it's time to make the fur. Tip some PVA glue into a bowl, then mix in a little water. Take your tissue paper, and cut it into little squares around 4cm wide. Scrunch a square into a ball, dip it into the glue then stick it onto Paddington's face. Continue until the whole plate is covered, apart from the muzzle. Stick tissue paper around the edge of each ear.

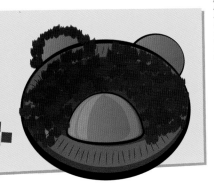

6. When the tissue paper fur is dry, Paddington needs one last coat of paint. Using the same dark brown as before, dab paint onto the tissue paper. You will need to do this carefully, so you get into all the folds without pulling the paper off the plate.

7. Cut a round nose and a bear mouth out of a scrap of black felt. Stick these onto Paddington's face, then add a pair of wobbly eyes.

8. Now all Paddington needs is a hat! Take a piece of red felt and stick it onto a rectangle of card. Flip the card over and draw out a hat shape. Carefully cut the hat out and stick it onto Paddington's head. Tilt the hat at an angle so that you can see at least one of his ears.

## BEAR BITES

Paddington is unusual because he is a sociable bear. Unlike *Ursa Marmalada*, most bears are solitary creatures. They roam alone across territories that can be as big as 200 kilometres square.

# Meet Judy Brown

Mr and Mrs Brown's elder child is going through a difficult phase. Judy is a sensitive teenager who is constantly being shown up by her parents. How can any girl maintain a basic level of street cred with a mum who calls her 'sweetie-pops' and a dad who still insists on holding her hand in public places? Add an irritating little brother and no wonder it can all get a bit too much sometimes.

When her family are driving her crazy, Judy's answer is to stick on her headphones and listen to her Chinese language tapes ... until Paddington comes to stay. But will his antics be enough to coax Judy out of her bedroom once and for all?

**" It's weird, it smells and it's embarrassing. "**

## BEAR BITES

Jonathan dreams of being an astronaut. He's got a secret ambition to become the youngest person to orbit space.

Jonathan is the youngest member of the Brown clan. He's a lively, curious child, despite his father's determination to wrap him up in cotton wool. In order to keep Jonathan safe, Mr Brown only allows his son to play with toys made when Mr Brown was a boy. Dusty train sets and worn yo-yos are all very well, but every boy needs some excitement once in a while.

Jonathan loves Paddington from the very first moment he sees him, sitting forlornly on his suitcase under a LOST AND FOUND sign. Having a real-life bear as a house guest is just as awesome as he hoped it would be! Jonathan doesn't know where Paddington's adventure will take him, but he can't wait to find out.

## BEAR BITES

Jonathan has a talent for construction. Paddington is very impressed when Jonathan uses his old-fashioned toys to build a moving, mechanical fairground.

**"Dad's always been boring and annoying."**

# Bear Buns

Even Mrs Bird has been inspired by her new friend Paddington! The elderly lady has devised an ingenious bread roll recipe. Each one looks like a little brown bear. Why not try making a batch? Mrs Bird's buns taste delicious with butter and marmalade.

Ingredients for 12 bear buns:
- 300g strong white bread flour, plus extra for sprinkling
- 1 teaspoon fast-action yeast
- 1 teaspoon salt
- 1 tablespoon sugar
- 175ml milk
- 2 eggs
- 50g soft butter
- Brown or black writing icing

Always ask an adult to help you in the kitchen!

1.  Tip the flour, yeast, salt and sugar into a mixing bowl and stir them together. Add the milk and one of the eggs, then carry on.

2.  As you stir, the ingredients will start to form a dough. Sprinkle some flour onto a clean worktop, then lift the dough out with your hands. Knead it for at least five minutes, until it is soft and smooth.

3.  Gently knead in the softened butter, making sure that it gets thoroughly spread through the mixture. Shape it into a ball, then work at it for five minutes more.

4.  Place the dough back in the mixing bowl, then drape a tea towel over the top. Tuck the bowl on a shelf in the cosiest corner of the kitchen, away from any draughts. Leave it there for two hours.

5.  Ask an adult to preheat the oven to 190°C/375°F/Gas Mark 5. Line two baking sheets with greaseproof paper. Now pull away the tea cloth and peep into the bowl – the dough should have nearly doubled in size!

6.  Divide the dough into 14 small balls. Put 12 of them on the baking trays, leaving lots of space between each one. Next use the leftover dough balls to make 24 little ears and 12 noses. Use a dab of water to stick two ears and a nose on to each bun.

7.  Leave the bears to stand for 20 minutes. Beat the last egg in a little bowl, then gently brush it over each bun. Ask an adult to place the baking trays carefully into the oven. The buns will need to bake for around ten minutes. When they have turned a lovely golden brown, your adult helper can take them out.

8.  Ask your adult helper to put the bear buns on a wire rack to cool. When they are cool, use a tube of writing icing to add two dots for eyes and a dot nose to each one. Delicious!

Make sure you keep the kitchen ship-shape – Mrs Bird is allergic to mess!

# Who Said That?

Mr Curry has been snooping again! The Browns' nosy neighbour can't help 'accidentally' overhearing other people's conversations. Who has he been eavesdropping on this time?

Draw lines to join the sentences up to the right speakers.

*Learn more about the characters - turn to the contents page to find their profiles!

1. "I'm going down the sewers tomorrow night and wondered if you wanted to come. It's a hidden world of mystery!"

2. "Batten down the hatches, there'll be a storm tonight!"

3. "It's called a 'Hard Stare'. My aunt taught me to do them when people have forgotten their manners."

4. "I'm a father and it's my job to protect this family."

5. "You're pulling my legs off! What a splendid idea."

6. "This is a cathedral of knowledge. Every major explorer has added to its collection."

A. MILLICENT

B. HENRY BROWN

C. MR GRUBER

D. MARY BROWN

E. PADDINGTON

F. MRS BIRD

When he's not taking his chances on the busy streets of London, Paddington often stops to think about Darkest Peru. It was a place where he could sit in his treehouse and eat marmalade all day long.

# Puzzling Peru

Do you know much about this faraway land? There are 15 words and phrases related to Peru hiding in this letter grid. Find each one and boost your geography know-how along the way!

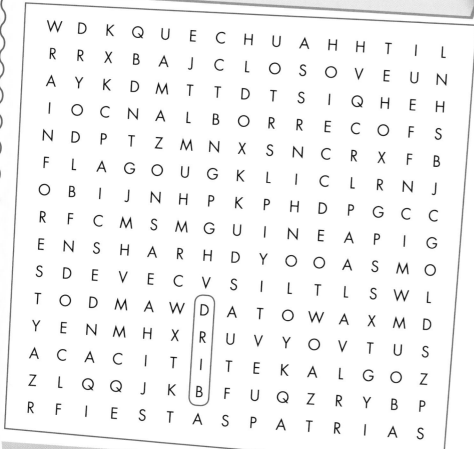

```
W D K Q U E C H U A H H T I L
R R X B A J C L O S O V E U N
A Y K D M T T D T S I Q H E H
I O C N A L B O R R E C O F S
N D P T Z M N X S N C R X F B
F L A G O U G K L I C L R N J
O B I J N H P K P H D P G C C
R F C M S M G U I N E A P I G
E N S H A R H D Y O O A S M O
S D E V E C V S I L T L S W L
T O D M A W D A T O W A X M D
Y E N M H X R U V Y O V T U S
A C A C I T I T E K A L G O Z
Z L Q Q J K B F U Q Z R Y B P
R F I E S T A S P A T R I A S
```

## ORCHID
Peru's climate is perfect for growing orchids. It can boast over 1,500 different types of this flower.

## GUINEA PIG
Peruvians call these 'cuy'. Guinea pigs are used in many traditional meals.

## GOLD
Peru is rich in natural resources. As well as gold, its lands are mined for silver, copper, lead and zinc.

## MACHU PICCHU
An ancient Incan mountain-top citadel that can be visited to this day.

## BIRD
Peru has the most bird species in the entire world. There are also huge numbers of butterflies.

## AMAZON
The world's largest tropical rainforest. Only Brazil has more Amazon jungle than Peru.

## POTATO
Wild potatoes first originated from Peru. There are now at least a thousand different types.

## QUECHUA
One of Peru's official languages. The others are Spanish and Aymara.

## RAINFOREST
The lush, natural ecosystem that covers nearly two-thirds of Paddington's homeland.

## NUEVO SOL
The currency (money) of Peru.

## ANDES
The majestic mountain range that runs through this South American country.

## CERRO BLANCO
The highest sand dune on the planet is Peruvian. It towers over the Sechura Desert.

## LAKE TITICACA
The world's highest navigable lake. It can be found in Southern Peru.

## FIESTAS PATRIAS
Every July, Peru celebrates its independence from the Spanish. The official celebrations last three days.

## LIMA
The capital of Peru and home to over a quarter of the population.

35

# I Spy!

**BEAR BITES**

Binoculars have come a long way since they were first invented in the seventeenth century – the latest models can take digital photos and record HD video!

Millicent always takes a keen interest in Paddington and his friends. Today she's been scouring the streets of London. Who has she managed to trap in her state-of-the-art, super-zoom lens? Identify the close-ups, then write labels for each one.

1.

2.

3.

4.

5.

6.

# Where's Our Bear?

Paddington Bear has disappeared! Can you help the Brown family find him? Their wayward guest could be anywhere in London. Use your boldest pens and pencils to design a MISSING BEAR poster.

Don't forget to colour your poster in!

# Lost
## in London

Start

38

Poor Paddington is somewhere in the capital city – lost, lonely and almost certainly in trouble! Can you help the Brown family track the young bear down? Weave a route through the London landmarks, avoiding the dead ends and blind alleys.

**BEAR BITES**

Underneath London's maze of streets, there are miles of buried waterways. One, the Tyburn river, even runs directly underneath Buckingham Palace!

Finish

# Paws for Thought

Montgomery Clyde, the explorer who discovered Paddington's aunt and uncle, was fascinated by the mysteries of nature. He made extensive field notes on every animal he encountered. His great passion was bears — such noble creatures!

Take a look through some of Clyde's notes. Has someone been tampering with them? Read his observations, then decide which ones are facts and which ones are fibs.

Check out the answers on page 61.

1. A male bear is called a 'sow'.

   Fact ☐     Fib ☐

2. Koalas look like bears, but they actually belong to the marsupial family.

   Fact ☐     Fib ☐

3. When they are sleepy, some bears make nests in tree branches to rest in.

   Fact ☐     Fib ☐

4. Bears are very clumsy animals.

   Fact ☐     Fib ☐

5. Female pandas raise their cubs on their own, without the male bear.

   Fact ☐     Fib ☐

6. An American black bear can run at speeds of up to 40 kmph.

   Fact ☐     Fib ☐

7. Sun bears have very long tongues.
   They use them to lick honey and bugs
   out of holes and other small spaces.

   Fact ☐     Fib ☐

8. There are over 20 main species of bear in the world.

   Fact ☐      Fib ☐

9. Every summer, a bear hibernates in its den.

   Fact ☐      Fib ☐

10. *Ursus arctos horribilis* is the scientific name for a grizzly bear.

   Fact ☐      Fib ☐

11. Bears that eat both plants and animals are called 'omnivores'.

   Fact ☐      Fib ☐

12. Black bears can live for more than 25 years.

   Fact ☐      Fib ☐

13. The giant panda is native to Madagascar.

   Fact ☐      Fib ☐

14. Pandas spend around three hours a day munching on bamboo.

   Fact ☐      Fib ☐

15. The smallest type of bear is the sun bear.

   Fact ☐      Fib ☐

# Marmalade Magic!

As far as Paddington is concerned there is only one thing that anyone can spread on their morning toast – marmalade! It's tangy, sweet and full of orange-y flavour. Paddington doesn't only eat it for breakfast – he won't leave the house without an emergency marmalade sandwich tucked under his hat!

Do you want to be a marmalade connoisseur, too? Here are Paddington's top ten facts about the fabulous, fruity spread.

**1.**
Marmalade has a very long history. Over the centuries its ingredients have been refined again and again. The earliest marmalades date back to ancient times. One of the oldest surviving recipes for marmalade was written down by Elizabeth Cholmondeley in 1677. She called the recipe 'Marmelet of Oranges'.

**2.**
The name marmalade comes from the Portuguese word marmelos, which was a type of paste made out of quince.

**3.**
In 1524, King Henry VIII received the first recorded gift of marmalade. It was presented to him by a man called Mr Hull from Exeter in Devon.

**4.**
There are lots of different types of marmalade – thick cut, thin cut, vintage and flavoured. Black marmalade is a type that has brown sugar or molasses added to it.

**5.**
Marmalade has many famous fans. The British prime minister Sir Winston Churchill, fictional secret agent James Bond and the explorer Edmund Hillary all loved the orange stuff.

**6.**

The World's Original Marmalade Awards are held every year in Cumbria. The winning entry is sold in London's food emporium, Fortnum and Mason.

**7.**

Most everyday breakfast marmalades that are bought use Seville oranges as their main ingredient. They are in season for just a few weeks every year, when they are picked and preserved.

**8.**

In Britain, marmalade is different from jam. As well as being associated with citrus fruits, marmalade usually contains fruit peel. In other countries, 'marmalade' can mean any type of fruit spread.

**9.**

One of the world's most famous marmalades is Robertson's Golden Shred. It has held a Royal Warrant since 1933.

**10.**

The first commercial producers of marmalade were the Keiller family of Dundee, Scotland. The story goes that James Keiller bought a batch of oranges from a ship recently docked from Seville. On its journey, the ship had been delayed by a harsh storm, causing its cargo to over-ripen. James and his mother Janet bought the fruit for a bargain price, then used it to make marmalade.

# Meet Mrs Bird

**" I gave up being surprised when they came up with the microwave oven. "**

## BEAR BITES

The no-nonsense pensioner does have a superstitious side. When trouble's afoot she feels things in her knees. They're especially useful for predicting the weather.

Mrs Bird lives with the Browns at 32 Windsor Gardens. She might be a little old lady, but she runs a tight ship. When she blows her whistle, everybody does as they're told! Mrs Bird's military precision comes from having had a husband who was in the Navy.

Mr Brown has the good sense to leave the day-to-day running of the house to Mrs Bird. Everything always goes like clockwork. She is allergic to mess and muddle, but when Paddington arrives, she takes the news in her stride. The canny old lady thinks that the loveable bear might be just what the Brown family needs…

## BEAR BITES

Mrs Bird can turn her hand to any household challenge – DIY, car maintenance and even welding!

*« My body had travelled very fast but my heart, she took a little longer to arrive. »*

Mr Gruber and Paddington have a lot in common. Mr Gruber had to leave his country when he was not much older than Paddington, arriving alone and frightened in London. Luckily a great-aunt took him in, but he soon learned that home means much more than just having a roof over your head.

Now that he's grown-up, Mr Gruber runs an antique shop on Portobello Road. Paddington loves it there. The shop is full of knick-knacks and curios, each with a story to tell. It's a place where the Brown family are always welcome. If they ask for his help he insists on serving them cocoa and buns – Mr Gruber finds that a serving of elevenses always makes things seem better.

# Paddington's Portrait

Paddington is a truly remarkable bear! It's high time that the Browns had a portrait of their newest family member to hang on the wall. Would you be so kind as to oblige? Sharpen a pencil, then carefully copy each square in the photograph below into the matching empty square on the page opposite. When you've finished, use coloured pens or pencils to bring the portrait to life.

Don't forget to sign your masterpie

Many of the great explorers made drawings of the creatures and plants that they encountered during their travels. The Natural History Museum has a big collection of art in its archives. It even has some botanical drawings from Captain Cook's journey on the HMS Endeavour between 1768 and 1771 – the first ever voyage devoted solely to scientific discovery.

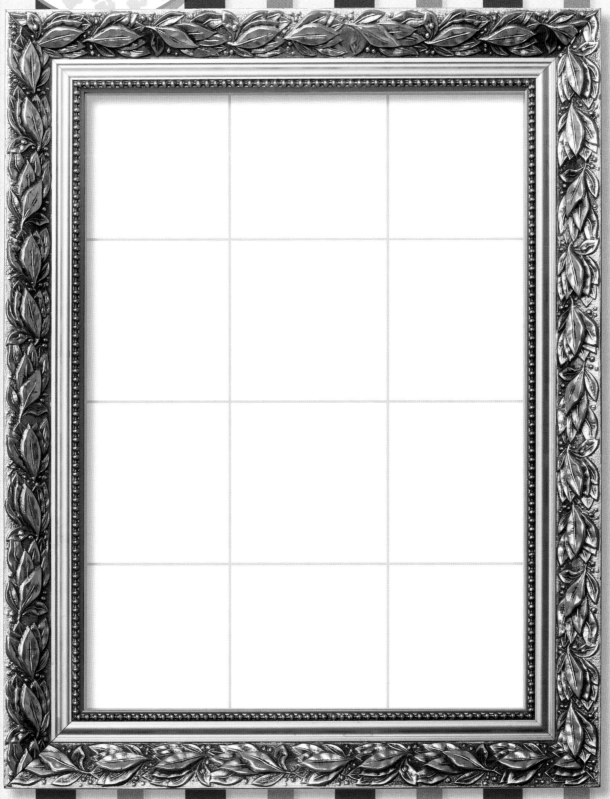

# On the Map

Would you be brave enough to pack a battered suitcase and set sail across the world, just like Paddington? This easy map make-it is a brilliant way of thinking about the places you'd like to explore. If you're lucky enough to visit any foreign lands collect postcards to remind you of your travels.

## You will need:

- An old noticeboard or cork tiles
- A world map (you can buy these cheaply from office supply stores) that will be smaller than the board behind it
- White sticker labels
- Bobble-topped pins
- Scissors
- Felt-tipped pens
- Coloured ribbons
- Postcards from trips

Peru

Take care with scissors and sharp pins. Ask an adult to help before starting this project.

1. Ask an adult to pin your world map on to the noticeboard or cork tiles, then mount it onto a wall.

2. For each of your dream travel destinations, take a white sticker label and carefully wind it around a pin. Snip the label into a flag shape.

3. Use your felt-tipped pens to write the name of the destination onto the flag. You could even add a little picture, too.

4. Find the destination on the map, then pin it in place.

5. Every time you manage to explore one of your dream destinations, be sure to buy a colourful postcard and mail or bring it home. Stick the postcard on the edge of your corkboard. Unfurl a length of thin ribbon, then pin it from the postcard to the flag place marker. Every time you look at the location on your map, you'll have an instant reminder of what it was like!

Brazil

## EXCITING EXPLORATIONS

France

What are your dream destinations?

Write them in here, and why you'd like to visit.

1. ................................................................................................
................................................................................................

2. ................................................................................................
................................................................................................

3. ................................................................................................
................................................................................................

4. ................................................................................................
................................................................................................

5. ................................................................................................
................................................................................................

Make a list of the places in the world you'd love to visit. Could it be the Great Wall of China, Sydney Opera House or maybe the rainforests of Peru?

Australia

**BEAR BITES**

The word 'map' comes from the Latin 'mappa' meaning napkin or cloth. Although maps have been used since ancient times, there are still some remote parts of the world that haven't been surveyed in detail.

All of the bears back home in Peru follow Paddington's progress with interest. What would they think of Millicent's devious bear-napping plans? Imagine a story about Millicent and Paddington, then write it on to the front page of their local newspaper. Don't forget to draw in the pictures, too!

# THE RAINFOREST GAZETTE

Lima, Peru

Price: 1 marmalade jar

.........................................................................................................

.........................................................................................................

## STOP PRESS! STOP PRESS!

Reported by...........................

WE CAN REVEAL TO OUR READERS THAT LUCY AND PASTUZO'S NEPHEW, YOUNG PADDINGTON BEAR, WAS IN THE MIDDLE OF A NAIL-BITING ENCOUNTER IN LONDON LAST NIGHT.

..............................................................
..............................................................
..............................................................
..............................................................
..............................................................
..............................................................
..............................................................
..............................................................
..............................................................

ALSO INSIDE:

# Perfect Manners

Whatever trouble he causes, Paddington has impeccable manners, many of them learned from *Friendly Advice for the Foreigner in London*, owned by his aunt and uncle. He is always polite, although he will deliver a 'Hard Stare' if someone really oversteps the mark. Read on for hints on how to improve your manners, and become as polite as Paddington.

### Greeting

The English are known for their 'stiff upper lip' and many prefer to keep themselves private. When you meet someone for the first time, wait until you are invited before using their first name. Never greet someone you don't know with a kiss, either! Start with a firm shake of the hand or paw.

### Punctuality

If you are invited for lunch or dinner at someone's house, it is polite to arrive either exactly on time or ten minutes' late (no matter how peckish you are!). This gives the host or hostess time to do their last minute preparations. Never show up early. This is as bad as being very late.

### Queues

English people take queuing very seriously indeed! They will wait patiently for as long as it takes, sometimes even camping overnight on the street. Visitors should never, ever push in on a queue. Queue-jumpers are looked down on by the whole of English society.

### Dining

When eating a meal, the English dine in the continental style. This means that the fork goes in the left hand and the knife in the right. The fork is held with the prongs down so that food is scooped on to the back of it. This can be a tricky skill to master, especially for bears.

### Funny noises

While it may be acceptable to burp and parp elsewhere, the English definitely frown on this sort of behaviour. It is deemed very uncouth. If you can't help making a noise in front of others, follow it up quickly with a clear 'pardon me!'.

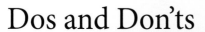

# Dos and Don'ts

**Don't**

- Wear your hat indoors, especially inside a church.

- Put your elbows on the table.

- Use the word 'toilet'. In polite society this is considered very crude. If you must use any word at all, 'lavatory' or even 'water closet' is much more acceptable.

**Do**

- Cover your mouth when coughing or sneezing.

- When enjoying a frothy drink, always lift the froth with a spoon. Drinking straight from the cup will give you a very embarrassing frothy moustache!

- Say 'please', 'thank you' and 'sorry'. These simple expressions can never be repeated enough.

**BEAR BITES**

Debrett's of Mayfair, London have been creating guides on etiquette since 1769. The publisher has even been mentioned in many famous books including *Vanity Fair* and *Brideshead Revisited*.

# Museum Marvels

Although it doesn't have an Ursa Marmalada, there are thousands of amazing exhibits inside the Natural History Museum. Many creatures on display there, however, are now sadly extinct. Some of these have died out due to natural threats, but lots of other species have suffered as a result of the impact of human beings on the environment.

### The dodo

The dodo is one of the most famous creatures to be eradicated as a direct result of contact with humans. The grey, flightless bird was native to Mauritius, but it quickly died out when colonisers destroyed its habitats. The last recorded dodo sighting was recorded in 1662.

### The Tasmanian tiger

The last Tasmanian tiger was caught in 1933 and placed in a zoo in Hobart, Tasmania, but it died three years later. It was a fierce meat-eater that looked like a wolf with stripes. The tiger was unusual because it carried its young in a pouch. Farmers hunted it to extinction in order to protect their livestock.

### The Baiji white dolphin

This Asian mammal is still to be declared officially extinct, but no Baiji white dolphins have been spotted since 2006. They are freshwater creatures with a blue-grey skin and a light dorsal fin. The dolphins used to swim in the Yangtze River in China. Over the last century, large numbers have been hunted or become caught up in fishermen's nets.

### The quagga

Imagine a chestnut brown zebra with stripes on its front quarters and soft white legs. The quagga was once common in South Africa, until its distinctive hide caught the eye of hunters. The only quagga to ever be photographed alive was snapped in London's Regent Park Zoo in 1870. In 1984, the quagga was the first animal to have its DNA analysed.

## Success stories

There's a lot of conservation work still to do, but it's not all bad news. Several amazing animal species have managed to come back from the brink of extinction and thrive once again. In the early 1900s, the koala was nearly wiped out. Over several decades, many koala reserves were established all across Australia. The population is now going from strength to strength. The American alligator, bald eagle and the bison are three more survivors that are now back in a place of safety.

## What can I do to help?

**1. Protect the wildlife near you**

Look out for the animals in your garden or park. We are all part of the same complex ecosystem – leaving food out for birds or creating a bug habitat can have a positive knock-on effect to countless other species!

**2. Lend a hand**

Support your local museum or animal centre; volunteer to beach clean or litter pick, or sponsor an endangered animal.

**3. Reduce, reuse, recycle**

Try to reduce the amount of rubbish you create and consequently less forest may be destroyed in areas where animal species are under threat.

BEAR BITES

An extinct animal is a creature that hasn't been seen in the wild for 50 years. Scientists estimate that the loss of species that we see in the 21st century is between 1,000 and 10,000 times faster than the natural extinction rate that would occur if there were no humans around.

# Meet Millicent

She may have a beautiful, blonde exterior, but there's more to Millicent than meets the eye. The Director of Taxidermy at the Natural History Museum has dubious ambitions and even more dubious methods. The moment she hears that a rare Peruvian Ursa Marmalada bear has landed at the docks, she is on a mission to find him.

Millicent has to be very careful. As one of the museum's most respected experts she can't be seen to be harming any living species. But if she should happen to stumble upon an old specimen that's got 'lost in the archive'? Well, that would be an entirely different matter! Millicent isn't used to being disappointed. Sooner or later, she vows to snatch Paddington and add him to her trophy cabinet.

> "As far as the tree-huggers who run this place are concerned, I'd never dream of stuffing a poor defenceless animal."

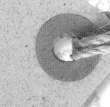

## BEAR BITES

When he starts spying for Millicent, Mr Curry gives her the code name 'Honeypot'. He refers to himself as 'Fierce Eagle'.

# Meet Mr Curry

Every street has a nosy neighbour, and Windsor Gardens is no exception. Mr Curry keeps a constant eye on the Brown family, staying up night and day if it's called for! When Paddington appears at number 32, he immediately grabs the neighbour's attention. As far as Mr Curry is concerned, bears spell trouble. They clog the drains with their fur and even throw buns at old ladies! And once one bear arrives, how many more will follow?

The Browns' greasy neighbour is just what Millicent is looking for – he's sneaky, sly and a natural lurker. Mr Curry is thrilled when she asks him to keep tabs on Paddington. From that moment, he puts himself on full-time bear-watch. He's determined to free Windsor Gardens of its 'Furry Menace.'

## BEAR BITES

Mr Curry is often out on his balcony, pruning his chives with nail scissors. It's the perfect spot for watching over Windsor Gardens.

" I keep an eye on the comings and goings and we've had a few unsavoury characters hanging around. There's even been a bear, a most unpleasant creature... "

# A Note from Paddington

Paddington has written a letter, especially for you. He's taken care to put the words in code so that it's safe from prying eyes. A bear in London never knows who might be watching!

It's up to you to decode Paddington's message. Use the alphabet key to decipher each line, writing each letter one by one into the space at the bottom of the page.

Dear Reader,

GSZMP BLF HL NFXS ULI HSZIRMT NB ZMMFZO! R'N DIRGRMT GSRH OVGGVI UILN NB UZELFIRGV KOZXV RM ZOO LU OLMWLM – NB ZGGRX ILLN RM DRMWHLI TZIWVMH. R SZEV OVZIMVW Z OLG ZYLFG GSRH DLMWVIUFO XRGB. NIH YILDM HZBH GSZG RM OLMWLM VEVIBLMV RH WRUUVIVMG. GSZG NVZMH VEVIBYLWB XZM URG RM... VEVM Z YVZI ORPV NV!

With lots of love,
Paddington x

| A | B | C | D | E | F | G | H | I | J | K | L | M | N | O | P | Q | R | S | T | U | V | W | X | Y | Z |
|---|---|---|---|---|---|---|---|---|---|---|---|---|---|---|---|---|---|---|---|---|---|---|---|---|---|
| Z | Y | X | W | V | U | T | S | R | Q | P | O | N | M | L | K | J | I | H | G | F | E | D | C | B | A |

Write Paddington's letter here:

\_ \_ \_ \_ \_ \_ \_ \_ \_ \_ \_ \_ \_ \_ \_ \_ \_ \_
\_ \_ \_ \_ \_ \_ ! \_ \_'\_ \_ \_ \_ \_ \_ \_ \_ \_ \_ \_ \_ \_
\_ \_ \_ \_ \_ \_ \_ \_ \_ \_ \_ \_ \_ \_ \_ \_ \_ \_
\_ \_ \_ \_ \_ \_ \_ \_ \_ \_ \_ \_ \_ \_ \_ \_ \_ \_ .
\_ \_ \_ \_ \_ \_ \_ \_ \_ \_ \_ \_ \_ \_ \_ \_ \_ \_
\_ \_ \_ \_ \_ \_ . \_ \_ \_ \_ \_ \_ \_ \_ \_ \_ \_ \_ \_
\_ \_ \_ \_ \_ \_ \_ \_ \_ \_ \_ \_ \_ \_ \_ \_ \_
\_ \_ \_ \_ \_ \_ \_ \_ \_ ...
\_ \_ \_ \_ \_ \_ \_ \_ \_ \_ \_ \_ !

# Answers

## Page 8
### Lost and Found
1. MARMALADE
2. APPLE
3. RADIO
4. YO-YO

Paddington's first friend in London is called: MARY.

## Page 9
### Taxi!
The correct route is: C

## Page 13
### Postcards to Peru
1. C
2. D
3. B
4. A

## Page 18
### Please Look After This Bear
1. MILLICENT
2. MR CURRY
3. HENRY BROWN
4. MRS BIRD
5. JONATHAN

Bonus bear brainteaser: PASTUZO.

## Pages 19-20
### Suitcase Surprise
1. 3 seashells
2. 6
3. the anchor
4. patterned
5. red
6. the plug
7. 4
8. the plant pot
9. 1

## Page 21
### Millicent's Mix-ups
1. ZEBRA and DONKEY
2. HELICOPTER and AIRPORT
3. SITUATION and COMEDY
4. JEANS and LEGGINGS
5. PICTURE and ELEMENT
6. BREAKFAST and LUNCH
7. MOTOR and PEDAL
8. CAMERA and RECORDER
9. ESCALATE and ELEVATOR
10. LABRADOR and POODLE

## Pages 24-25
### Tea-time Teaser

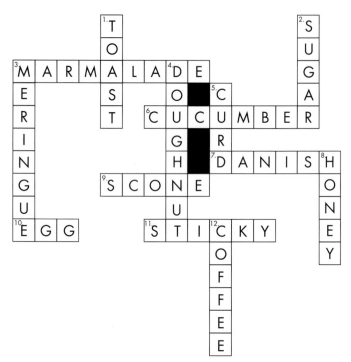

## Page 34
### Who Said That?
1. D
2. F
3. E
4. B
5. C
6. A

## Page 35
### Puzzling Peru

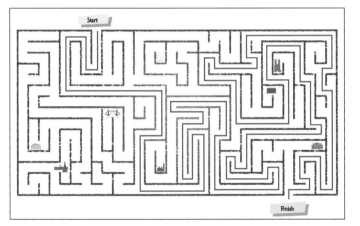

```
W D K (Q U E C H U A) H H T I L
R R X B A J C (L O S O V E U) N
A Y K D M T T D T S I Q H E H
I (O C N A L B O R R E C O) F S
N D P T Z M N X S N C R X F B
F (L A G O U G K L I C L R N J
O B I J N H P K P H D P G C C
R F C M S M (G U I N E A P I G)
E N S H A R H D Y O O A S M O
S D E V E C V S I L T L S W L
T O D M A W D A T O W A X M D
Y E N M H X R U V Y O V T U S
(A C A C I T I T E K A L) G O Z
Z L Q Q J K B F U Q Z R Y B P
R (F I E S T A S P A T R I A S)
```

## Page 36
### I Spy!

1. MR GRUBER
2. HENRY BROWN
3. JONATHAN BROWN
4. JUDY BROWN
5. PADDINGTON
6. MRS BIRD

## Pages 38-39
### Lost in London

## Pages 40-41
### Paws For Thought

1. Fib. A male bear is called a 'boar'.
2. Fact.
3. Fact.
4. Fib. Bears have an excellent sense of balance. They can even stand on their hind feet!
5. Fact.
6. Fact.
7. Fact.
8. Fib. There are actually only eight living species.
9. Fib. Bears hibernate in the winter.
10. Fact.
11. Fact.
12. Fact.
13. Fib. Giant pandas come from China.
14. Fib. Pandas spend at least 12 hours a day eating bamboo!
15. Fact.

## Page 59
### A Note From Paddington

Thank you so much for sharing my Annual! I'm writing this letter from my favourite place in all of London – my attic room in Windsor Gardens. I have learned a lot about this wonderful city. Mrs Brown says that in London everyone is different. That means everybody can fit in... even a bear like me!